"This third book in the series was a fantastic read. I loved the relevancy to ___ seeing around us in the home and in society. It's really accessible to all, and ___ daughter loved it. It really inspired me to have more detailed conversation: ___ aspects of technology that we sometimes do not have discussions about."
Daniel Bowen, Technology Strategist at Microsoft
@dan_bowen

Children are excellent users of technology but they are often passive users. *The Digital Adventures of Ava and Chip: Smart Home* explores a wide variety of technology found around the home. The story will help children become more inquisitive about the technology they see and use on a daily basis. In turn, this will hopefully inspire more of them to explore this technology, and perhaps even consider a future career working with and designing similar tech in the future.
Becky Patel, Parent and Head of Education and Learning for Tech She Can
@BeckyPatel86

An excellent journey into the digital realms of a smart home, elegantly explained and beautifully illustrated. Young people will easily identify with the technology that's being portrayed in this lovely story. A brilliant way of introducing young folks to the concept of a fully connected smart home. A must for every school and home educator.
Russell Prue, Bett Radio Host & Broadcaster
@RussellPrue

Much like the children in my classes, I am always excited to pick up a new book in the *Ava & Chip* book series. *Smart Home* proves no exception. This story seamlessly introduces a whole host of technologies through the power of storytelling. Not only that, but my students see a relatable family interacting with and being curious about technology, compelling role modelling that has certainly inspired my students to follow suit!
Naomi Gale (she/her), EdTech Specialist

The Digital Adventures of Ava and Chip: Smart Home is an exciting new book that any child can enjoy. It tells a modern-day adventure story and introduces plenty of new tech terms that both children and adults can learn and enjoy. My children and I really enjoyed reading this book together and I highly recommend it as a great gift.
Faith Ruto, Mom of two, Coach & Author
@faithrutot21st www.faithruto.com

"I have a surprise for you," Mum says to Ava and Chip.

"Oh, wow!" says Ava, and raises her eyebrows.

"Great!" exclaims Chip. "What is it, Mum?"

Mum smiles and says, "Next week we'll be returning to the **SMART CITY OF DIGITA**, and this time we'll be staying for a few days in a **SMART HOME**."

"A **SMART HOME**," gasps Chip. "What's that?"

"Let me explain," replies Mum. "A **SMART HOME** is much like ours, but uses lots of **TECHNOLOGY** that's all connected to the **INTERNET**. **DEVICES** in the home are controlled automatically, and you can connect to the home to control the **DEVICES**."

Ava, Chip and Mum go to the city by train, where they then walk to a bus stop.

At the bus stop, Chip asks, "Mum, how do we pay?"

"Good question," replies Mum. "I have a 'SMART bus card' for both of you. I'll use my 'SMART bus' app and pay on my phone." Mum then gives Ava and Chip their cards while saying, "When the bus arrives you need to place your 'SMART bus card' on the SCANNER. The bus will then know the start time of your journey, and how many people have boarded the bus."

A short while later, the bus arrives and the trio board the bus, SCANNING to get on board.

As they travel, there is a voice on the bus announcing arrival at each stop. Ava notices that there is a **DIGITAL MAP** in the bus displaying the route. She nudges Chip.

"Look at our route," says Ava quietly.

"That's the **ALGORITHM** the bus is following," interjects Mum.

"Our destination is in seven stops," says Chip.

Both look out of the window and observe the city as they travel. About twenty minutes into the journey, the voice on the bus says the next stop is **OLYMPIA**. Ava and Chip start to get very excited.

Mum turns to them. "Have you got your bags and everything?" she asks. Both Ava and Chip nod. Mum then says, "Don't forget, as you get off the bus you'll need to **SCAN** your '**SMART** bus card'. This will let the bus know that you've ended your journey. It will also be able to calculate how much the bus ride costs."

After a short walk, they arrive at their accommodation. As they reach the door, Ava and Chip are amazed when Mum finds a **QR CODE** on her phone, and then places it on a **SCANNING** machine beside the door. The door swings open.

"I love **TECHNOLOGY**," says Ava. "Mum, how does it work?"

"Ah, when I made the booking **ONLINE** I was **EMAILED** a **QR CODE**. This is just like a physical key. It has all the **DATA** and **INFORMATION** it needs stored within the **QR CODE**. This then opens the door."

"Oh, wow!" says Ava. "Thanks, Mum."

"QR" in "QR" code means "Quick Response"! It is made up of black-and-white squares that can be read by a machine.

Try scanning the QR code above to visit Ava and Chip's website.

Ava and Chip are so excited. They quickly drop their bags on the floor and head off to explore the house. As they wander around, they discover lots of unusual things about the house...

- The TV can be turned on by **voice activation**.
- They can play music by speaking to a **device**.
- There are lots of **cameras** in the house.

"Ava, wait here," says Chip, as he runs back to the front door and presses the doorbell.

Ava looks at a **SCREEN**, and realises that she can see Chip. She presses a **MICROPHONE** button and says, "Hello." Chip laughs loudly. "I can see you," she says. They both start speaking to each other through the **SMART DOORBELL**.

Mum is really pleased that Ava and Chip are so curious. "Let's see if we find anything else," she says. Ava and Chip can hardly contain their excitement. As they continue to explore the house, Mum shows them lots of new and exciting **SMART HOME** features.

- Smart meter – used to measure energy usage such as gas and electricity in the home.
- Smart thermostat – to control the temperature in each room.
- Smart kitchen – with lots of **smart appliances** such as a **smart** fridge, which has built-in **cameras** and you can remotely monitor what's in the fridge when not at home, via an **app**.
- Smart plugs – when **appliances** such as kettles and hairdryers are plugged in, if you forget to turn them off, you can do this remotely from an **app**.
- Smart lighting – to change the colour and brightness of lights, and also to time how long lights are left on.

Ava and Chip are particularly excited with the last feature. They hurriedly go to their bedrooms, and experiment by changing the colour of the lighting.

Mum follows them. "This is called 'mood lighting'," she says.

"It makes me feel happy and peaceful, Mum," says Ava, changing her light to a warm yellow.

"I'm feeling energetic," says Chip, turning his light a bright purple. They are both laughing as they continue to play with the lighting features.

"When all of these **DEVICES** are connected to the **INTERNET** from homes and buildings around the world, this is a part of what is known as the **INTERNET OF THINGS (IOT)**," explains Mum.

How many **devices** do you use that connect to the **Internet**?

They all go into the living room. On the table is a **SMART DEVICE**. "This **DEVICE** can play music, state the time, make calls, tell jokes, offer a weather report, and much more," explains Mum.

"Oh, wow," they both say. As they continue to explore the house, they find and interact with **SMART GADGETS** in each room. They soon come across a cupboard in the hallway. They open it and find a tall broom, a dustpan, and a small **APPLIANCE**.

"Ooh, ooh, what's this, Mum?" calls Chip. Mum joins them beside the cupboard and removes the **APPLIANCE**.

"Ah, this is a **ROBOT** vacuum cleaner," Mum says as she turns it on, and demonstrates how it works. Ava and Chip follow it around. As Chip stands in front of it, they both ask lots of questions...

- How does it know where to go?
- How long does it clean for?
- How does it not collide with objects?

"The vacuum uses **LASER** navigation called **LIDAR** and lots of **SENSORS** to help it in find its way around a room," explains Mum.

"That's so cool," Chip says.

"I agree," says Ava, clapping her hands in delight. They both then continue to explore the **SMART HOME**.

After a while, Ava says, "This house is really great, Mum. Can you tell me more about how it works please?"

"OK," says Mum. "Go and get your brother, and I will explain it to both of you. You see, there is lots of **TECH** being used in the house."

- **Internet** connectivity.
- **Wi-Fi** connectivity.
- **Voice Activation Technology** when speaking to **devices**.
- **Sensors** to control heating temperature, air conditioning, smoke detectors and carbon monoxide detectors.

"In fact, there are lots of **SENSORS** in the house including a 'Leak **SENSOR**'. This **SENSOR** detects leaks in bathrooms, or any room with water, and reports back to the owners."

"Ah," says Ava. "**SENSORS** are very important. We've learned about them on our trips.

"Am I right in saying that the home security system uses **CAMERAS,** and also if someone enters the house while we are out, the 'motion **SENSOR**' is activated, setting off the alarm?"

"Yes, well said," responds Mum. "I'm proud of your knowledge!"

"But if we're not home, how will we know if the alarm's going off?" asks Chip.

"This **APP** on my phone is used to control and monitor the alarm," replies Mum. "We can control everything using an **APP**. For example, we can also adjust the temperature in the house remotely, so when we get home, it's just right for us."

Then Chip says, "I can think of another way that **TECH** is used. My teacher at school showed us how we can speak to the **COMPUTER,** and then the **COMPUTER** can translate 'speech to text'. Also, you can speak in one language and special **SOFTWARE** will translate what you say into another language. In the clubs at school we speak to children from other countries and use this **TECHNOLOGY**."

"Very impressive," says Mum. "I'm glad you've made the connection. Well remembered, Chip."

"Let's go outside," says Mum. As they stand outside, Mum explains, "The house is energy efficient. It captures most of its energy from the sun. The windows are specially designed to capture solar energy. There are also solar panels on the roof."

"That's amazing," says a very impressed Ava. "Mum, I have a question. What happens if you cannot capture enough sunlight?"

"Ah ha!" responds Mum. "Well, the house is still connected to a main energy source and can use this as a **BACKUP**."

"Thanks, Mum," responds Ava. Thinking for a bit, she says, "It's exciting the ways that **TECHNOLOGY** can be used. I'll tell my friends when I'm back at school."

After some more time exploring, Mum calls Ava and Chip downstairs. "What would you like to eat tonight?" she asks.

"Pizza!" they both reply very quickly!

"I thought so," says Mum, and smiles. She then uses an **app** on her phone to order pizza and other treats for them. They then settle in to watch a film on a large home cinema system in the living room. Mum looks at Ava and Chip as they are eating and enjoying the film. She smiles as they are both very content.

Mum knows that later Ava and Chip will discover **sensors** embedded in their beds. These will record the quality of their sleep.

Tomorrow will be another day of questions and surprises.